# Because We Stayed Home...

## A Story of Hope

### Paula Shue Winfrey

Amazing Things Press

Book design by Julie L. Casey

ISBN 978-1949830460

Printed in the United States of America.

For more information, visit
www.amazingthingspress.com

# Dedicated to

The brave people all over the world helping to fight the Coronavirus Pandemic,

Those who are fighting for their lives,

Those who recovered,

Those who lost their fight.

We will not forget you.

IT FELT LIKE EVERYTHING
IN THE WORLD
CHANGED OVERNIGHT.

People were talking about a mysterious virus.

TV was filled with
maps, charts
and sadness.

IT WAS VERY SCARY.

We were asked to stay home if we could.

Schools closed all of a sudden.

Having no school sounded pretty good...at first. But this wasn't like a regular vacation. It was just weird.

Many businesses closed.

PEOPLE WERE AFRAID TO GO ANYWHERE.

*We missed our family and friends.*

EVERYTHING WAS DIFFERENT.

But because we stayed home...

Our teachers and parents found new
ways to teach us.

**We learned how to Zoom in little boxes on
our computers, phones and tablets.
Great-Grandma is still figuring it out.**

Our parents and
family became our
teachers from home
and we learned how
to work things out
together.

But we missed people. A lot.
We couldn't be with our teachers or friends.

We couldn't be with lots of the people in our lives.

But because we stayed home...

# People showed us they still cared—

## IN WONDERFUL, COLORFUL WAYS.

WE HAD TO BE CAREFUL IF WE WENT
SHOPPING. AND FINDING TOILET PAPER
WAS LIKE DISCOVERING BURIED TREASURE.

Staying 6 feet apart from each other felt so lonely and far.

We were nervous to do normal things.

But because we stayed home...

# People helped each other.

Boy, did they ever!

We were asked to wash our hands often and **NOT** touch our face, so we wouldn't get sick or make others sick.

That was **really** hard to do!
Do you know how many times a day we usually touch our face?  A gazillion!

But because we stayed home...

We discovered that 20 seconds to wash our hands takes as long as singing the *ABC*'s or the chorus of *Let It Go*!

(C'mon people, admit it, you know the words.)

And our hands have never been cleaner.
We helped keep the virus from spreading.

Many people could work from home...

**But many others lost their jobs.**

But because we stayed home...

People worked together like they were part of a team.

Who knew there were so many ways to make a face mask?

Lots of businesses figured out clever ways to stay open.

We could still get things with drive-thru, carry out and delivery. It was actually super handy.

Some family members needed to work away from home. They worried that they might bring home the virus.

People had to be careful to get rid of the germs before they came home.

And others stayed away from home to keep their families safe, but they missed their loved ones.

No hugs are definitely no bueno.

But because we stayed home...

# Families stayed connected anyway.

The virus
couldn't stop us.
It was tough, but
we were tougher.

*People were asked to stay away from public places.*

**We couldn't go to movies, eat at restaurants or play at parks.**

Graduations, weddings and special events were cancelled.

**We couldn't even go to church.**

But because we stayed home....

# Church came to us.

## We celebrated life in other ways.

## And you know what? We still had fun.

# Entertainment, sports and large gatherings were cancelled.

ShowBiz 18.11, 01-Apr-2020

**Over 100 American TV shows stop filming due to COVID-19 pandemic**

Updated 19:22, 01-Apr-2020

CGTN

Popular TV series including "Stranger Things," "Grey's Anatomy," and "The Morning Show" have halted production due to the outbreak of the novel coronavirus

HOME > MUSIC > NEWS   Mar 31, 2020 10:49am PT

**CMA Festival in Nashville Is Canceled for 2020**

By Chris Willman

The CMA Festival, the world's largest country music gathering, has been canceled for 2020, rather than trying to push the mass gathering set for June in Nashville to a later date in the year.

### TV shows changed.                Concerts stopped.

### Sports took a break.

## It felt like nothing was okay. Though not for long.

## Because we stayed home...

Famous people brought the entertainment to
us from their homes and it was amazing.
They live just like us.

We could laugh. We could dance. We could make
funny videos. We could feel normal again.

Some people were like *superheroes*.

They did the scary jobs. They took care of the rest of us.

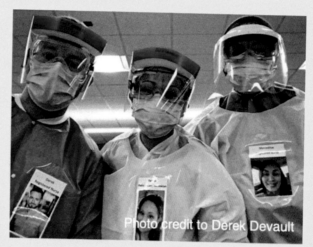

They were very tired, but kept on going.

Superheroes don't stop until their job is done.
Some got the virus while they worked hard.
Some bravely died trying to help others.

Because we stayed home...

We made it easier for our heroes by not spreading the virus.

Our leaders asked us to help flatten the curve.

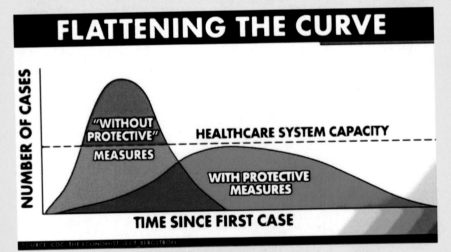

It's hard, but important to do.
They can't fight the virus alone.

Things are getting better in lots of places, but many people still need our help. Our communities are counting on us to continue doing our part.

Photo credit to WPLG-Local 10 News

We can be superheroes, too.

It takes everyone to stop the virus.

Because we stayed home...

 Most of us didn't get sick.

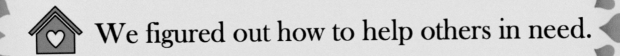 We figured out how to help others in need.

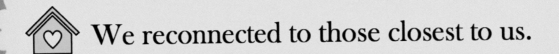 We reconnected to those closest to us.

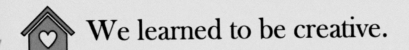 We learned to be creative.

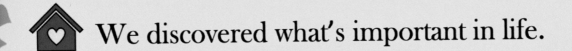 We discovered what's important in life.

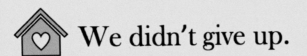 We didn't give up.

We helped save lives.

# Life will go on.

We may be apart, but we're doing it **together**.

# Stay strong. We've got this.

## Because we stayed home.

The charities listed below are a place to start.
If we all do a *little*, it will accomplish **BIG** things.

www.feedingamerica.org
www.samaritanspurse.org
www.shcfb.org

To find a list of more top-rated nonprofit
charity organizations check out:
www.charitynavigator.org
Thank you!

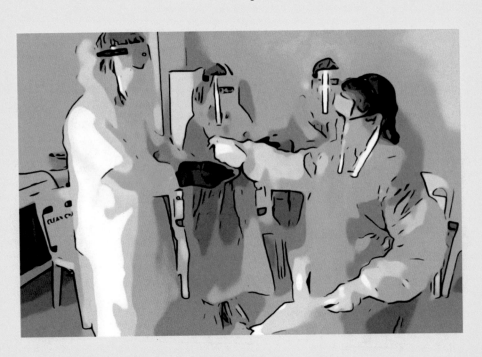

# About the Author

Paula Shue Winfrey is a writing late-bloomer. She took the roundabout way to publishing her first book by first raising four fascinating people with her jack-of-all trades husband, Dana Charles. Along her journey, Paula's been an administrative assistant, a daycare owner, and for 22 glorious years, found her passion as an elementary school teacher. Still a hip happenin' gal, she's finding time to create, enjoy grandmahood, and appreciate a beautiful life.

You can contact Paula at:
stjoecpl@sbcglobal.net
https://www.facebook.com/paula.shuewinfrey
Instagram- silverliningsdecor
Twitter- Paula Winfrey@stjoecpl

# Message from the Author

Thank you for taking the time to read our book.
I would be honored if you would
consider leaving a review for it on *Amazon*.

Check out more amazing Children's Books from

Amazing Things Press

amazingthingspress.com

Made in the USA
Coppell, TX
06 December 2020